BACH FLOWER ESSENCES
AND THE PATTERNING OF WATER

If the doors of perception were cleansed every thing would appear to man as it is, infinite.
For man has closed himself up, till he sees all things thro' narrow chinks of his cavern.

William Blake (1757-1827) *Marriage of Heaven and Hell*

Bach Flower Essences

and the Patterning of Water

JULIAN BARNARD

FLOWER REMEDY PROGRAMME

2016

Published by
Flower Remedy Programme
Walterstone, Hereford HR2 0DX, UK

ISBN 978-0-9561455-5-0

Designed and typeset in Arno
at Five Seasons Press, Hereford, UK,
and printed on Five Seasons recycled paper
by TJ International, Padstow, Cornwall, UK

This is the moment to say thank you to the many people who have helped me come to this small book with an appetite for new ideas and investigation. I will start with Nickie Murray who inspired with confidence and trust all those years ago. And in what has been 40 years since I first met her at the Bach Centre there have been many friends along the road with whom I have worked and shared: Joy Southgate, Greg Vlamis, Graham Challifour, Sandra Hill, Romy Fraser, Vicky Lee, Vivien Williamson, Gérard Wolf, Mike Booth, Beth Bruno, Luciana Chammas to name but a few. I would like to thank both Judy Howard and Stefan Ball at the Bach Centre for extending the hand of friendship in recent years. Healing Herbs has been in business for more than 25 years and in that time there have been countless meetings and discussions with people from all around the world; without them I would have given up long ago. It might be appropriate to thank my teachers but they have all been teachers. The staff at Healing Herbs also have been wonderful and stimulating companions to work with. My family and relatives have been so supportive but I will give a special mention to Kelly Vassie for introducing me to biosemiotics and in a similar vein Alex and Taraka Barnard have sent links to information from the academic world in which they work. I would like to thank Martine, their mother.

The images and illustrations are mostly photographs that I have taken. But where they come from other people I have tried to give full and proper acknowledgement in the text. In particular I would like to thank Herb and Annie Lewis for the lambs, Mike Booth for the labyrinth design based on the depiction in the Hereford Mappa Mundi, Sandra Hill for Chinese calligraphy, Schumacher College for the mandala, Barry Shaw for help with 'Free Thyself', friends in Japan for the photographs of Torii, Glenn Storhaug for the letterpress images. Some others have been found online and adapted without full and proper attribution. The book was designed and typeset by Five Seasons Press: many thanks Glenn.

St Thomas's Well, Herefordshire

Water has been around for far longer than any of us and will be around long after we are gone. We can run alongside it for a while and absorb it into our life process as does every other living thing — and then we must leave it to continue its journey.

When water emerges from an underground source it emerges with a history of interactions with the material world. Constantly changing its form, adapting, merging, submerging and emerging again and again.

This special fluidity of water enables it to change very rapidly. But everything in the world is in flux. From the fast electrical activity of neurons in the brain to the achingly slow erosion of mountains.

When we seek to interact with this world we can either look to control, confront, objectify and manipulate it. Or we can endeavour to step alongside it, to merge with it and go with its flow.

The plants that Dr Edward Bach collected were, of course, similarly in a process. A process of growth. The making of his remedies was a merging of several of these material processes. When he brought plant and water together he was not seeking to impose the one upon the other. He was enabling a correspondence to take place between the plant, the water, the sun and himself.

If we take this a step further we could see the bottled essence itself not as a 'finished' product, but as a furtherance of the flow of materials. The essence, the glass, the dropper are continuing in movement, each with its own time signature but still walking together along a path.

Next, a practitioner of the remedies could be seen as being alongside their client, not in confrontation, but travelling the path together. Julian has often described many ways in which that special correspondence can take place.

And again, once taken, the remedy continues in flow with the body, and it manifests in the knowledge and the experience of the person moving into their future.

So too, over longer periods of time, plants evolve, and the practice of research and development with the remedies has to be a part of this evolution.

The whole process has no beginning and no end. For a while Dr Bach stepped into the arena and absorbed, and was absorbed by, the life forces he found.

And he founded a movement that today lives and breathes, and accompanies us along our way.

Mike Booth
Hereford February 2016

When you open this book and begin to read you are joining a family. A family of friends and colleagues who together honour Dr Edward Bach. He was born 24th September 1886. So 2016 will be his 130th birthday and 80 years since his death in 1936. As a family we can come together to commemorate these anniversaries. And why? It is not just that we value and respect a great man from the past. It is also because we are his grandchildren. We are the third and fourth generation of people who have been heir to his discoveries and ideas about health and plant medicine. Usually, if you say grandchildren you are speaking of a bloodline, genetics and common ancestry. But although Bach did have a daughter he is now remembered more for the sharing of ideas than the inheritance of a family line. And why do I say this? Because, from the beginning, as soon as Dr Bach discovered something new, or had an idea which was relevant to health, he published all the information. In other words he gave his ideas to the world, freely and without any control, restraint or bias and certainly no trademarks.

So in the 1930s 1940s or 1950s anyone was free to share that inheritance. Dr Bach's ideas were never to be controlled, limited or subject to vested interests of any one person or group. His book *Free Thyself* states this over and over again. We are all free to be part of the forward-moving wave which promotes a self-developmental approach to learning about ourselves.

This may be a rather long explanation of why I believe that we are all inheritors of Dr Bach's ideas. But it is important in the context of what I want to say next. From the very beginning Bach was in contact with people in different countries. Indeed, in 1934 when he decided to make Olive and Vine as new essences in the group of the Seven Helpers, he asked colleagues in Italy and Switzerland to make the mother essences for him.[1] If nothing else this gives the lie to the idea that only mother essences prepared in one particular

---

1 Weeks, Nora, *The Medical Discoveries of Edward Bach* C. W. Daniel, 1940, page 102.

Free Thyself

EDWARD BACH, *Physician,*

M.B., B.S., M.R.C.S., L.R.C.P., D.P.H.

This can be read in *Collected Writings of Edward Bach*, FRP, 1987
Courtesy of The Board of Trinity College Dublin

location or by one particular person can legitimately be called Bach flower remedies.

And before I go any further I need to clarify one or two other matters about the naming of things. In the 1930s, when Dr Bach practised as a qualified medical doctor, the notion of a remedy was anything which might help someone to make an improvement in health. Today a remedy can only be used to describe something registered as a medicine in law. So we must all get used to speaking of flower essences and not flower remedies.

And another thing before I move on: it really doesn't matter whether you say Bach or Batch. The pronunciation is never as important as its meaning. Maybe you remember the George Gershwin song:

> You say tomato, I say tom<u>a</u>to . . .
> You say either I say <u>ei</u>ther,
> — either, <u>ei</u>ther, neither n<u>ei</u>ther,
> let's call the whole thing off . . .

Now I know that this may be lost in translation and that is rather my point. If you are in Brazil and all you think about is how to pronounce the word then you are missing out on a lot of opportunities. If you are in Japan and can only discuss who is allowed to do what, then you are missing the point too. This subject is not about control: it is about freedom. And, as Dr Bach said: *to gain freedom, give freedom.*[2] So let's start there.

Let's step away from orthodoxy and stop searching for the correct answer and go exploring. And what shall we explore? Well, the most fascinating thing to explore is the form and function of the plants and how they relate to the whole world in which we live.

---

2 *Collected Writings of Edward Bach*, FRP 2007, page 126.

Form and Function is rather an abstract idea so let us begin with specific details. For me there have always been two particular questions: why did Dr Bach choose these plants to make his essences and how do the essences work? The first question has been looked at quite closely in terms of the plant's structure and how the elements combine — Earth, Water, Air and Fire — and become expressed in the plant in Root, Stem, Leaf and Flower. This needs some explanation both in terms of the plant's structure but also in terms of the elements.

The root represents the past, the family, and the physical dimension of earth. Plants are almost always rooted in the earth and the roots store the starch from the past season to allow for the future development of that individual. We can see that most obviously in root vegetables which we eat like carrots or parsnips. Roots are also the means by which the plant takes water and minerals from the land and generates the whole process of growth. As such it can be said to link to the family insofar as roots and the earth provide sustenance for growth and development, just as parents do in a family.

The stem represents the Water element which works as circulation and distribution of energy — which is equivalent to the emotional state. It is water or sap which circulates in the stems and links the roots with the leaves. So it is the carrier of both energy and experience within the metabolic process of the plant. Why does this link to the emotional state? Because it is the driver of the internal processes of life. The emotional responses we have are like the fuel which we burn to create action and direction, be that fight or flight, hatred or love.

The leaves represent the lungs of the plant where the Air element is exchanged — equivalent to the mental circumstances. The leaves are perhaps the most essential functioning part of the plant because this is where photosynthesis takes place (although all parts are interdependent). They are responsive to outside stimulus and can change behaviour according to changes in circumstances like heat and light within the seasons. As such they are linked to the mental state where we process incoming information and can decide to modify our actions.

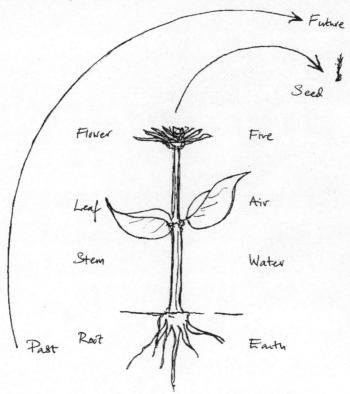

And the flower is the element of Fire which represents the potential for change and transformation. The element of fire simply because it is the agent that brings about the most immediate and visible change of state: set fire to paper and it becomes reconstituted as ash, water vapour and gases. The flower is the future through the generation of seeds where genetic characteristics combine through pollination by outside agencies, be they insects, wind, water or animals. Pollination brings about a change in state within the flower through the development of a new life form: the seed.

The fifth element or fifth factor is the seed itself. It speaks of the future and encapsulates the whole of the plant's life in potential for new growth and new development.

Clematis growing on the cliffs at Cromer

The way in which these four elements combine in the plant's life cycle gives information about the balance and predominance of the elements at work. If the plant or tree has deep roots then there is strong attachment to the earth. The converse is equally true if the root structure is slight and tenuous. Where the stems are small the emotional content is relatively weak; if dry there is emotional detachment since the water element is missing. The size of the leaf indicates the mental capacity while complexity of form suggests complexity of expression. A simple leaf suggests the opposite.

Consider Impatiens for example. (Incidentally, I think the

La Chicorée Endive.
Lat. *Cichorium.* Ital. *Cichorea.* Esp. *Almerones.* Angl. *Succory.* Allem. *Hindlöfft* Oder *Cichorien.*

Chicory print, Nicolas and Genevieve Regnault, 1774

evidence is clear enough that this first flower essence, discovered in 1928, was Dr Bach's own remedy type).[3] A study of this plant shows how its form embodies the idea of the Impatiens remedy state as described by Bach:

> Those who are quick in thought and action and who wish all things to be done without hesitation or delay. . . . They often prefer to work and think alone, so that they can do everything at their own speed.
>
> [*Twelve Healers & Other Remedies* 1936]

---

3 Weeks, Nora, *The Medical Discoveries of Edward Bach*, C. W. Daniel, 1940, pp 135-140.

Impatiens stem and leaves

The root structure is minimal: that is why the plants only grow close to water. And in this case it is significant because the Impatiens type of person is not strongly linked to the earth, to family and the past. Impatiens is an annual and fast growing, reaching up to three metres in height. The stem is upright, strong and structural: so the Impatiens person has strong clear, directed emotions. The leaves are simple and spear-shaped: technically they are called lanceolate because they look like the blade of a lance or spear. So the thinking is also simple, clear and directed. The flowers are complex, delicate and hanging on the point of balance. This suggests that the transforming quality of Impatiens is tenderness and relaxation – Dr Bach calls it forgiveness and speaks of the need for gentleness and peace.

Impatiens flower

The same structural analysis can be applied to the other Bach essences. Scleranthus with its alternating stem-form speaks of ambivalence and changeability. The simple, soft barb of the leaf looks the same as the stem and since both are equally green both are involved in photosynthesis. It points to the fact that in this plant the emotional and mental states are similar, the simplicity of choice, yes or no:

> Those who suffer much from being unable to decide between two things, first one seeming right then the other.
> [*Twelve Healers & Other Remedies* 1936]

Scleranthus

The sensitivity of the Agrimony type links to the hairy leaves, looking outward and sensitive to others and the environment:

> Though generally they have troubles and are tormented and restless and worried in mind or in body, they hide their cares behind their humour and jesting.
>
> [*Twelve Healers & Other Remedies* 1936]

Chicory with its deep roots stays close to the family and the past:

> ... they tend to be over-full of care for children, relatives, friends, always finding something that should be put right. ... They desire that those for whom they care should be near them.
>
> [*Twelve Healers & Other Remedies* 1936]

Chicory root

Agrimony's hairy stem and leaves

Clematis with its lack of structure and drifting seeds is 'longing to be blown away and start again' as Dr Bach writes in *Free Thyself.*[4]

Clematis seed

---

4   *Collected Writings of Edward Bach*, FRP, 2007, page 130.

Later he writes of the Clematis person as:

Those who are dreamy, drowsy, not fully awake, no great interest in life.

[*Twelve Healers & Other Remedies* 1936]

Clematis seed head

This kind of analysis can be applied to all the 38 Bach essences,[5] even to Rockwater which is not a flower at all. And with Rockwater we might begin to look at the second question: how do the Bach essences work?

This is not a quick and easy subject and in this context I can only begin to look at the factors which point to what actually happens when we take an essence. It might be thought that there is some chemical, active ingredient in Impatiens or Chicory which initiates

5 See Barnard, Julian, *Bach Flower Remedies Form & Function*, Lindisfarne Books, 2002.

a subtle chemistry in me when I take the drops. But with Rockwater that cannot be the case since the essence is just water. Indeed with each of the 38 Bach essences there is nothing which can be analysed and regarded as a chemical trigger which initiates bodily change.

I do not want to hold you in suspense with this question although I do want to invite you to think. If there is no active chemistry involved then what is in the essence? Often people speak of an energy which alters or modifies the energetic system of the person receiving it. But all the evidence points to the fact that there is no energy present in the essence. Energy is used to make the mother essence – the energy of the sun in the sun method and the energy of fire in the boiling method. (You will remember I am sure that Dr Bach wrote about two different methods of making the mother essences when he published his discoveries in 1936). But that energy, be it sun or fire, is not present after the preparation is complete. And that is why I would suggest that what is present in the essence is not energy but information.

METHOD OF PREPARATION

Two methods are used to prepare these remedies.

SUNSHINE METHOD

A thin glass bowl is taken and almost filled with the purest water obtainable, if possible from a spring nearby.

The blooms of the plant are picked and immediately floated on the surface of the water, so as to cover it, and then left in the bright sunshine for three or four hours, or less time if the blooms begin to show signs of fading. The blossoms are then carefully lifted out and the water poured into bottles so as to half fill them. The bottles are then filled up with brandy to preserve the remedy. These bottles are stock, and are not used direct for giving doses. A few drops are taken from these to another bottle, from which the patient is treated, so that the stocks contain a large supply. The supplies from the chemists should be used in the same way.

The following remedies were prepared as above: Agrimony, Centaury, Cerato, Chicory, Clematis, Gentian, Gorse, Heather, Impatiens, Mimulus, Oak, Olive, Rock Rose, Rock Water, Scleranthus, the Wild Oat, Vervain, Vine, Water Violet, White Chestnut Blossom.

Rock Water. It has long been known that certain wells and spring waters have had the power to heal some people, and such wells or springs have become renowned for this property. Any well or any spring which has been known to have had healing power and which is still left free in its natural state, un-hampered by the shrines of man, may be used.

28

THE BOILING METHOD

The remaining remedies were prepared by boiling as follows:

The specimens, as about to be described, were boiled for half an hour in clean pure water.

The fluid strained off, poured into bottles until half filled, and then, when cold, brandy added as before to fill up and preserve.

Chestnut Bud. For this remedy the buds are gathered from the White Chestnut tree, just before bursting into leaf.

In others the blossom should be used together with small pieces of stem or stalk and, when present, young fresh leaves.

All the remedies given can be found growing naturally in the British Isles, except Vine, Olive, Cerato, although some are true natives of other countries along middle and southern Europe to northern India and Tibet.

The English and botanical name of each remedy is as follows:

*AGRIMONY	.	.	Agrimonia Eupatoria
ASPEN	.	.	Populus Tremula
BEECH	.	.	Fagus Sylvatica
*CENTAURY	.	.	Erythræa Centaurium
*CERATO	.	.	Ceratostigma Willmottiana
CHERRY PLUM	.	.	Prunus Cerasifera
CHESTNUT BUD	.	.	Æsculus Hippocastanum
*CHICORY	.	.	Cichorium Intybus
*CLEMATIS	.	.	Clematis Vitalba

29

Bach, Edward, *The Twelve Healers & Other Remedies*
C. W. Daniel, 1936

Now that is quite difficult to prove because contemporary scientific thinking only accepts that which can be measured or weighed. Let me be precise about this. When we talk about information – let's say an idea or a message – it has no measurement. An idea has no weight, size or dimension. We might say 'this is an *important* idea' but that doesn't change it in terms of measurement. Interestingly, a point in geometry has no dimension since it is, by definition, a position – the intersection of x, y and z axes but no

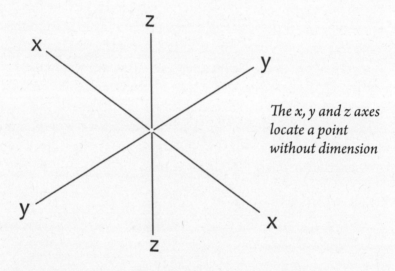

The x, y and z axes locate a point without dimension

more than that. Some would argue that something which is not capable of being measured can only be speculated about but not proven. The 2015 Nobel Prize for Physics was awarded to scientists who demonstrated that neutrinos have mass and can therefore be said with certainty to exist.

A young person who worked at Healing Herbs got into some trouble on just this point. His physics teacher had said: 'Nothing exists in reality which cannot be measured or weighed.' He replied: 'So the laws of physics do not exist.' He did not do well in the exam! But I would like to think that he may have another future which includes practical human experience.

Going back to information: I would like to ask you a few questions. What do you think this image means? OK. It's straightforward. It is a 'stop sign'. But there are people who ignore the stop signs. It is not a sign which forces you to stop. It just advises you to stop: it is information.

How you and I read that information depends upon how we feel. And, how we feel depends upon what information we read.

Now we are getting there, or we are closer. If we follow on with this thought we can see that everything is information. And we interact with it all the time. External information is read through our five senses – what we see, feel, hear, smell and taste.

Interestingly we also speak of a sixth sense – which maybe we use to gather information about another kind or another level of reality.

Those five are all sources of external information. But we also have internal sources of information in our body and mind. My imagination is a source of information; my internal organs are also a source of information. It is generally agreed that we have five vital organs: brain, heart, liver, kidneys and lungs. And the skin is often regarded as the sixth vital organ which mediates with both the inner and the outer world. The skin and internal linings of the body are a continuous membrane. So perhaps the skin acts as a sixth sense.

Where am I going with this? Well, take a simple example such as a cat which is frightened by something so that its hair stands up on end. What makes it do that? It is information which triggers a biochemical response in the cat's skin. Sometimes we can know what frightened the cat and sometimes we can't. Actually we also react in a similar way ourselves – at least we may have a reaction on the skin even if we do not have as much hair as we used to!

Interestingly, this relates to what is called somatization[6] where a person has physical symptoms such as stomach aches in the absence

6   Wilhelm Stekel, an early follower of Freud, coined the term in 1924. Born in Austria he moved to London in 1938, two years after Bach's death.

of a known medical condition; the symptoms caused by emotional or psychological distress. And the somatization process can act in reverse when in a hospital or care home psychological comfort can be gained through the sensory pleasure of being able to stroke a cat or a dog. Another aspect of this reaction to information is explored in the science of biosemiotics. Although this is dismissed in some circles as more philosophy than true science it deals with the process by which life forms read the signals or information from both the internal and external environment.[7]

All this points to the fact that we have various reactions to information. So let's return to the Bach essences and what information they may contain. Because it is the most challenging let's begin with Rockwater. Dr Bach said this is a state of mind which develops over time when we allow a theory or system of faith to rule our lives, when we become hard-masters to ourselves in the belief that it will set an example for others to follow. He says that we can use 'any well or spring which has been known to be a healing centre and which is left free in its natural state'.[8] I believe he first made this essence when he was in Abergavenny in the summer of 1933. He stayed at *The Swan Hotel* and may have used a nearby spring, close to St Mary's Priory. Its Welsh name was *Ffynon y Garreg* which means Spring of the Rock – hence Rockwater.

So, taking water from this holy well he set out the bowl in clear uninterrupted sunshine. He says it took about one hour to make the mother essence. Usually we leave the bowls with flowers for three hours. When preparing any of the flower essences we use similar fresh spring water and during the three hours there are visible changes taking place.

---

7 'Biosemiotics is the study of the myriad forms of communication and signification observable both within and between living systems. It is thus the study of representation, meaning, sense, and the biological significance of *sign processes* – from intercellular signalling processes to animal display behaviour to human semiotic artefacts such as language and abstract symbolic thought.' Donald Favareau, *Essential Readings in Biosemiotics*.

8 *Collected Writings of Edward Bach*, FRP, 2007, page 72.

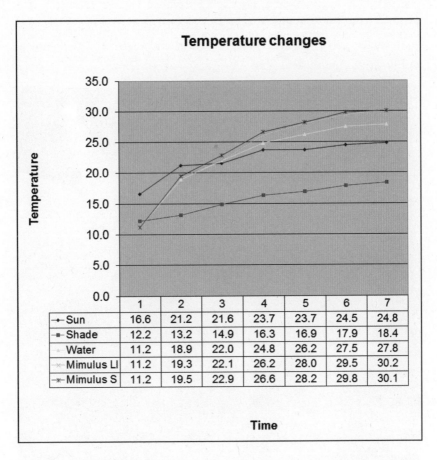

Temperature changes

	1	2	3	4	5	6	7
Sun	16.6	21.2	21.6	23.7	23.7	24.5	24.8
Shade	12.2	13.2	14.9	16.3	16.9	17.9	18.4
Water	11.2	18.9	22.0	24.8	26.2	27.5	27.8
Mimulus Ll	11.2	19.3	22.1	26.2	28.0	29.5	30.2
Mimulus S	11.2	19.5	22.9	26.6	28.2	29.8	30.1

Time

Here you can see the relative temperature changes between the air, the water and the essence preparations taken at thirty-minute intervals. The two Mimulus readings were a large and small bowl.

What actually happens during this time? When the water issues from the ground it is generally about 10 degrees Celsius, feeling cool on a warm, sunny day. Condensation often clouds the outside of the bowl at first but gradually in the sunlight the temperature rises and may reach 28 or 30 degrees. Something remarkable occurs in this process which can be observed every time when essence making. As the temperature rises small bubbles appear in the bowl. Quite simply this means that the rise in temperature and exposure to the sunlight must expel gases from the water. In addition to the bubbles the water in the bowl begins to sparkle and shine. We see a prismatic effect as light is refracted in the water – it has stars of yellow, red, purple and blue.

Chicory essence after three hours

In the case of the sun method this change can be observed by anyone. And that is one of the best things about this kind of science – the science of observation – it does not require the construction of a scientific theory or hypothesis, an esoteric language or a fantasy about unseen forces or spirits. The science of observation is open to anyone who cares to observe. One of the things which can be seen with the sun method is the way the water surface forms a pattern around the flowers. Is this the visible expression of a pattern which is imprinted in the water?

Rock Rose at 9 am

Rock Rose at 12 noon

Oak flowers at the end of an essence preparation

Rock Rose

Cerato

Mimulus

With the boiling method it is a little more difficult to see what takes place. But the fire from beneath the saucepan has the effect of reversing the elements. By this I mean that in the sun method the fire is above and the air is expressed out into the water. In the boiling method the fire is below and the water is expressed out into the air. This is about the ordering of the four elements. When the energy of the sun is contained within the earth as fossil fuel (formed in the geological past from life forms such as trees or marine animals) we use it as fire. What was once the fire of the sun returns towards its source.

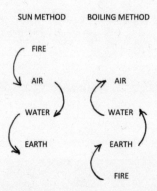

To elaborate on this idea for a moment, it does suggest something of the difference between the essences made by these two different methods. Dr Bach named 38 essences in all between 1928 and 1935. First there were the Twelve Healers, then the Seven Helpers and in 1935 the Second Nineteen. He spoke of the 'new nineteen' as being 'more spiritualized'. In a letter to friends written in July 1935 he wrote:

> There is no doubt that these new remedies act on a differ-
> ent plane to the old. They are more spiritualized and help
> us to develop that great inner self in all of us which has the
> power to overcome all fears, all difficulties, all worries, all
> diseases.[9]

9 *Collected Writings of Edward Bach*, FRP, 2007, page 34.

Perhaps what he is describing is 'the power' to change, transform and develop as a result of difficulties overcome. In this way these essences in the Second Nineteen point to a kind of metamorphosis of the individual in terms of emotional responses. This is brought about through the boiling method and the action of fire from within the earth.

Larch prepared by the boiling method

Leaving aside what mechanical science may or may not accept let's focus back upon what observational science can demonstrate: what we observe to be true. The reversal of the energy flow is always clear to see, not just as steam but in the dancing vapour with oils and traces from the plant which hovers above the surface of the water.

Interestingly, when we filter the essence after making there can be dramatic tongues of fire which flicker in the sunlight.

Filtering the mother essence

With both the Sun Method and the Boiling Method Dr Bach recommends that we use fresh water 'if possible from a spring nearby'.[10] This is a vitally important part of the essence-making process. We should consider what it may mean for the water to have issued from inside the earth, from the darkness of the rock. It always seems to me that this water is new born; like any new-born it is a *tabula rasa* or blank sheet without information or patterning from the past. Of course with a new-born infant there is the question of memory within the cells, informational coding from the genes and memories from the time spent in the womb. Perhaps these can be looked upon as unconscious. At the moment of birth a new process begins: imprinting. This occurs from the very first contact. Imprinting is a well-known term in psychology and refers to the rapid learning process which occurs, for instance, when a young animal acquires behavioural characteristics from its parent or whatever may be its first moving contact.

I had this experience once, many years ago, when walking under the cliffs on the Isle of Skye in north-west Scotland. I came upon a new-born lamb, still wet from birth but alone, without its mother. I could not leave it for a certain death on the seashore. So I picked it up and, with it cuddled in my blue anorak, scrambled up the cliff. There, at the top, was a field full of sheep. So I set the lamb down, saying: 'Off you go and find your mother.' Back came the plaintive bleat: 'You're my mother now!' And it followed me across the grass. That is imprinting, though whether the process was the first contact of life on life or just the colour of my coat I do not know. If you are interested to learn more on this subject it is worth reading about the work of Konrad Lorenz.

You might want to learn what happened next. I took it to the farmer who, of course, looked after it.

Now this process of imprinting takes place with every new life, so a million times a moment. It seems clear to me that imprinting is a process of recording information in the early stages of life experience. While the story of the lamb is an analogy, we can

---

10 *Collected Writings of Edward Bach*, FRP, 2007, page 72.

*Twin lambs
five hours old*

Impatiens

say that the first contact was a permanent record of the earliest experience. Information was being recorded. The same, or a similar thing, happens to the water when exposed suddenly to sunlight. Information is being recorded.

So we must ask: what information is being recorded?

In the case of a flower essence it is the flowers. The flowers work with the element of fire, like the sun, and that represents the potential for change. But of what, or to what? If the flower was Impatiens we might think that the gentleness and balance of the flower was there. But it actually includes the whole narrative of what the plant is in its essential being. It includes the whole image of the form and function of that species, the story of its life and the patterning of its life force.

If we look specifically at Rockwater this becomes a little more difficult to define. What you might ask – or I can ask it for you – what is the pattern of life force for water in a holy well?

There are no quick answers to this. In part it is the whole land-scape of the place, the day, the moment of becoming. It is also something to do with the very nature of water, how it behaves and changes. Water flows around an object, always taking the path of least resistance and moving slowly but surely back to the sea where individuality is lost and mixed into the ocean of being.

Looked at in this light it is easy to see why Dr Bach speaks of Rockwater as leading to 'the realisation of *being* not *doing*, . . . of quietly and gently doing a little in the Great Plan'.[11]

Once, I was with a group of visitors from Japan, showing them the places where Dr Bach may have found the Rockwater essence. One person said, 'well, if you use fresh spring water to make all the essences then there is something of the Rockwater essence in each of the 38 essences.' And, of course, that is true. When we make Chicory or Vervain the characteristic information from the plant is there. And the information and patterning are taken up by the water as a new *pattern of life force*, a new beginning. This can

11 *Collected Writings of Edward Bach*, FRP, 2007, pages 96-7.

dissolve old structures and patterns, just as the water ultimately dissolves the rigid structures of rock.

It is one thing to observe the form and function of the flowering plant, to see how its gesture describes what it is. We must then ask how this information is recorded in the bowl of spring water? And in what language? I speak English, you speak German but what is the language of plants? And how might we learn that language? The language they use is how they grow — their form and structure. They speak the language of what they are. And we need to use all our senses to perceive that.

Elm flowers

Some experimental work has attempted to record how changes can occur in water. In 1924, following advice from Rudolf Steiner, Ehrenfried Pfeiffer (1889-1961) developed the technique of sensitive crystallization. The crystals he created formed different patterns from different plants. Years later Masaru Emoto (1943-2014) also developed crystallization images recording 'emotional energies'. In Switzerland in the past decade similar work has been done by Visionlab Soyana and by The Stuttgart Aerospace Centre.[12]

---

12 https://www.youtube.com/watch?v=cWLPFK3sXdw

Plate I.

Photographs 3/5 natural size

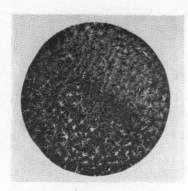

Fig. 1 Cu Cl₂ 20%
copperchloride alone
     without any addition
     (transmitted light)

Fig. 2 Cu Cl₂ 25%
     + 1 drop of waterlily-flower
        extract

Fig. 3 Cu Cl₂ 25%
     + 1 drop of extract from
        agava americana

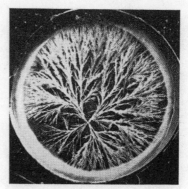

Fig. 4 Cu Cl₂ 5%
     + 1 drop of chamomile-flower
        extract

Sensitive Crystallization from Ehrenfried Pfeiffer

Soyana Visionlab

This is where we can enter controversy and can easily be met with rejection by conventional science. And I cannot claim any expertise in this subject other than the practical experience of essence making for the past three decades. We know for sure that when temperature rises water expands. And with the increase in temperature there is an increase in the agitation in the water molecules. Ultimately, if the water reaches boiling point it encounters phase change and liquid becomes gas. Energy is the essential factor in this.

I believe that as a part of the process of warming and increased agitation the spaces within the molecules of H_2O absorb information.[13] This may be connected to the so-called bunny-eared

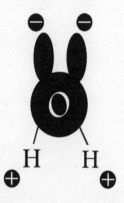

structure of H_2O and it may be linked to the constantly forming and breaking of the bonds between hydrogen and oxygen which occur, so we are told, at the rate of a trillionth of a second. (From this we can conclude that water is anything but stable.) Indeed it seems likely that this process takes place even without heat by virtue of the action of light on water.

When we begin such discussion we might reference Jacques Benveniste and the 'memory of water' experiments.[14] We then get

---

13   For more information see Chapter 2 'The Wonder of Water' in Sue Lilly's book *The Essence Practitioner*, Singing Dragon, 2015.

14   Chaplin, Martin, http://www1.lsbu.ac.uk/water/memory_of_water. html 2007, 2016.

caught up in the controversy surrounding homoeopathy and many other contentious practices. So let me say that, at this moment, there is no demonstrable scientific explanation for how water comes to take up the information present at the moment of essence making. But then we do not have a scientific explanation for how and why the lamb was imprinting upon my blue coat. But that imprinting certainly took place.

Let us suppose then that the mother essence does contain some particular information and that the information is carried by the water molecules. Somehow it is dispersed throughout another liquid when one or two drops of the essence are added. And I do have to admit that does sound strange. But then if we add a drop of coloured dye to clear water it will colour everything. It is impossible then to take some of that water which does not contain a part of the dye. This thought is an echo of Dr Bach's words from 1933 when he speaks of a drop of cochineal colouring a four ounce bottle of water.[15]

5.   Does it matter if I do not take the doses regularly now?   I am forgetting to take them?

        A very good sign. We should not eat, unless we are hungry and the body calls for food. We should not need medicine unless we are ill, so when we forget to take it, we may be sure that the necessity for it has passed away.

6.   How is it that one or two drops can do good? It seems such a minute dose.

        Just as the bite of that tiny insect, the gnat, can do great harm, so one drop of the remedy from a beneficent plant can do great good; just as one drop of cochineal will colour a four ounce bottle of water, so will also one drop of remedy make potent several ounces of fluid.

7.   Does it matter if I mix two or three remedies together in the same bottle?

        Very often this is necessary, should several states seem to predominate, such as fear, weakness and restlessness. (Mimulus, Centaury, Agrimony).

So the information is carried through from the original mother-essence-making event to the moment when I open the vial and take some of the information into me. But the question arises:

---

15   *The Healers and Helpers Newsletter*, No. 2, November 1933. Not currently republished.

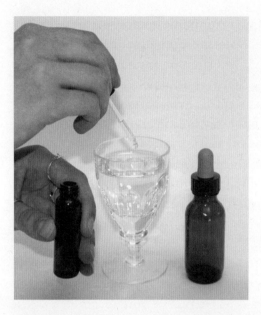

how do I read the information when I take some drops of this essence? I think that we read this information much as we read or receive sensory information. There is, if you like, a message in the water. The message is written in the language of the plant, and it is carried by the messenger which is the essence.

In an attempt to explain how this could work we need to take one more step into a new idea: the passive force field. An active force field is powered by energy – an energy which could be damaging if you encounter it. Electricity generates a force field and if I am careless I may get to know the force of it. Indeed every living thing generates a force field and it is something which we can measure by science – it is an indicator or proof of life. But a passive force field cannot be measured. It can be sensed, read, understood but it cannot be measured. It may help to consider a few examples of a passive force field. Architecture is a passive force field – if you enter a cathedral the structure is designed to influence your state of mind but it does so in a passive way.

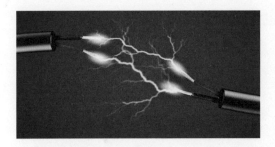

Symbols are a passive force field since they carry associations and ideas which we interpret from the visual perception.

Gloucester Cathedral [Photo David Iliff]

Heian Shrine, Kyoto [Photo Daisuke Takahara]

Torii in Japan indicate the entrance to a sacred space, a place of transition.

Hakone Motomiya Shrine, Kanagawa [Photo Kaoru Kobayashi]

Tohdo Shrine,
Kumamoto
[Photo Kizashi Saito]

Ana Hachimangu Shrine,
Tokyo

[Photo Tomoe Akiba]

The swastika evokes immediate reaction in the viewer

The Mappa Mundi in Hereford Cathedral has a labyrinth drawn on the island of Crete. Walking such a path takes one on the journey through a passive force field of contemplation. Interestingly the labyrinth comes close to describing the 19th of the 38 Bach flower essences: Wild Oat which is about orientation and finding our true path in life.

Labyrinth model by Mike Booth

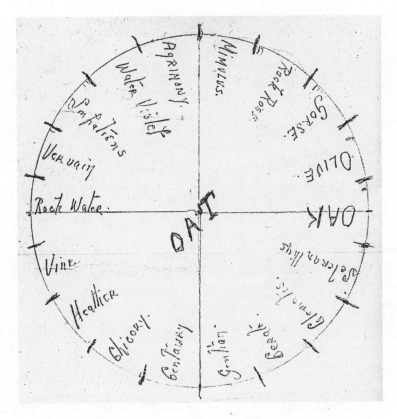

Dr Bach's diagram places Wild Oat in the centre of the circle

Mandala courtesy of Schumacher College

Geometrical designs within the mandala represent the universe and may be used to establish a sacred space in the mind. Here the passive force field can help to create the experience of balance and spiritual unfoldment. In that sense it is like the opening of a flower where the numbering and geometry determine the very structure of the plant's growth.

The geometry of Star of Bethlehem which is 6 + 6 + 6 + 1

Jeremy Pfeiffer 2010

Another expression of the passive force field is seen in the Cymatics experiments of Dr Hans Jenny. He used acoustic vibration to create patterns of infinite variety and complexity. Putting sand, powder or water on to a metal plate he caused variation in the patterning through an oscillator. This concept can be extended into more general use of movement and posture as a way to learn through experience in the body rather than theory in the mind. Any physical movement used as a spiritual practice, such as Yoga or Qi Gong, is based upon the similar idea of creating a passive force field through posture and movement. This in turn influences us as a life form.

Works of art can also influence us, but in a passive way. The painting makes no *active* intervention but it can carry a powerful message. The same is true of all kinds of images, of writing, books even, anything which can carry an idea.

Chinese calligraphy conveys more than the meaning of the word Dragon.

In the process of preparing a Bach flower essence we have a receptive medium (the water) an activating force (the sun) which transfers information from the living force field of the flower. This information is written into the water and retained there as a passive force field. It is this passive force field which is in the bottle. And when we take a few drops of the flower essence we receive the information.

We still have much to learn about the way that we exchange and use information. We need to be an active force field in order to read a passive force field that much is clear. This means we need to be alive. But it seems unlikely that we need to develop any particular skills in order to respond to information. And it is not a gift which belongs to any one species or race. We can illustrate this with the commonplace experience of knowing when someone is looking at you. This 'gaze detection' stimulates a particular part of the brain and is attributed to peripheral vision. But it can occur even if we are not looking in that direction or have our eyes closed. And it is not limited to human on human since the gaze detected could be a squirrel in the tree outside the window who watches, alert for danger. We suddenly have the feeling that we are being watched and look up to see the squirrel.

Cerato

Another commonplace is thought transference. It is something that we all experience but rarely talk about: knowing when someone is thinking of us or knowing what someone else is thinking. It can be an exchange of emotional information without words or contact. Although these things usually fall at the first fence of scientific experiment that does not mean that they do not exist. Like precognition, where the reasoning of science says that something cannot be known before it has happened, many of us have direct experience of a reality beyond the confines of scientific materialism.[16] I had just that experience as a youth when I dreamt the names of two horses who won their races the next day.

So what happens when we take an essence? Usually we open the vial and put two drops into a glass of water or take the drops directly into the mouth. This small amount of water enters a system which is itself liquid: so the information is immediately transferred to the whole body, just as Dr Bach described in relation to cochineal (see page 43). If it is difficult to understand how this happens we might consider how the liquid system of the body (we are about 70% water) can transfer chemical information rapidly – asparagus will make urine smell within 30 minutes. Chemical drugs can act even more swiftly. Blood circulates around the body in about 60 seconds carrying oxygen and all the complex chemistry to every living cell. So the information in the essence can be carried to the brain in moments. That is not to say that the brain is the only part of the body which can be receptive to the information in a Bach flower essence. The information may act as a catalyst to modify the action of any organ and initiate a chemical reaction. A simple example would be the way that Rock Rose can bring calm to someone in panic with high pulse rate and fast breathing. I have seen this happen with a small child in distress after being stung by a bee.

Interestingly there are some people who do not actually take the essence in liquid form. They may go to the flower, think about it or use a photograph which carries the same information or idea. Looking at the flower images also offers another approach to diagnosis. The details of colour and form enable us to respond without words. When we choose an image, either because it attracts

16   See D. H. Lawrence, *The Rocking Horse Winner*. Harper's Bazaar, July 1926.

Centaury

or repels us, we are working with an intuitive brain function. This can often prove helpful when working with children – they may make a choice without knowing why they are attracted to the photograph.[17] It can also work well when there are language problems, no matter what the reason may be. I learned about this process in 1990 when first working with photographs of the Bach flowers. Someone who was visiting the UK was in great distress and rather than ask questions through a translator I gave her the book with pictures and asked her to make a selection. She chose a few essences such as Cherry Plum and Sweet Chestnut which I might have guessed at. But why, I asked myself, had she put a tag by Centaury? When Dr Bach's description was translated she burst into tears saying: 'That's me, that's me exactly'. And how one might ask could that have happened? The pictures can speak the powerful language of the heart.

Sometimes such a selection can take place in a *reverse* manner. In the early years, when Dr Bach had just published *The Twelve*

17   Seedlings of Hope project in Cambodia, 2012. Charity work undertaken by Susan Fletcher and Vivien Williamson.

Healers, he showed the book to his sister and invited her to choose one of the essences. She read the text and commented that she could identify with them all, except Mimulus.[18] She was adamant that she was not like that. But that was the one her brother Edward had prepared for her to take. The story does not tell us whether she was later able to identify with the Mimulus state of mind – timidity and fear.

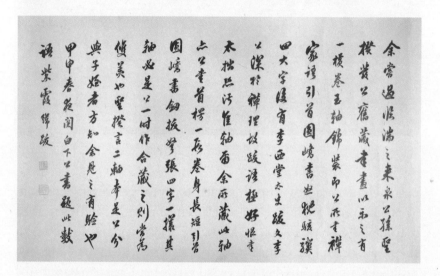

Part of the Buddhist Surangama Sutra (Neung Um Kyung) eighteenth-century Korean written in Chinese running script. Courtesy of The British Museum

The efficacy of the Bach flower essences depends upon two things: the clarity of the message and our ability to read it. That being the case, how do we read the passive force field? In the same way that we read a book. We allow the patterning to communicate with us in a meaningful way. I have a memory of a visit to the Shanghai Museum, where a calligraphy scroll arrested my attention. Of course I could not read it but the clarity of the message was so calming, balanced and tranquil that I still resonate with the memory. Indeed it was a little bit like the gentle and calm message of Impatiens.

---

18   Audio tape interview conducted by Gregory Vlamis.

Our ability to read the message is truly not altered by the facts of who made the essence. When people say 'this essence is better than that essence' or 'these are the true and original Bach essences' it is all very subjective. If the mother tincture is made according to the original directions of Dr Edward Bach it will be a genuine and original Bach essence. To claim some special superiority because of the name on the label is nonsense. It is like saying that my pen is better than your pen. But what matters is what you write with that pen. The important thing is the quality of the message, not whose name is on the pen.

The clarity of the message can be understood in another way. The first impression may be bright and clear but it may be that the image can become distorted or lose definition by repeated dilution or by interference. Repeated dilution refers to the limit placed upon the number of times in which the original stock concentrate can be watered down. If the original information was clear in the mother tincture and that is diluted 1 part in 400 to make the stock bottle (original stock concentrate) that works well but we might question if the message is still as clear if it is diluted to 1:100,000 as in a 5x homoeopathic dilution. For the avoidance of doubt it must be stated clearly that genuine Bach flower essences are not prepared homoeopathically.

Interference is different. It describes the way in which the original image may be distorted or changed by outside agencies. Electro-magnetic interference is perhaps the easiest to understand. There are various wavelengths which affect us all. These vary from radio waves which are long, slow and relatively harmless, to gamma waves which are high speed and destructive. In the middle part of the spectrum is visible light. But the light which writes the information into the mother essence water can also scramble the message if there is exposure to strong and constant light for some duration. That is why we always keep the essences in a cool, dark place, use amber glass and ensure that the liquid is not exposed again to light or radiation more than is necessary. Short wave gamma rays (as used in radiotherapy for instance) cause a powerful disruption to all forms of patterning. But there can also be interference by other

Sonnet 65

Since brasse, nor stone, nor earth, nor boundlesse sea,
But sad mortallity ore-swaies their power,
How with this rage shall beautie hold a plea,
Whose action is no stronger then a flower?

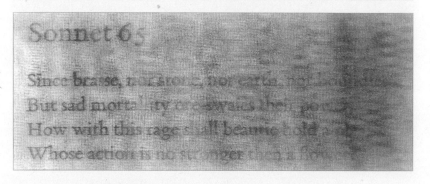

*An original letterpress print of Shakespeare's sonnet
becomes distorted by repeated copying*

energies where the information is distorted by what we could describe as over-printing. Interference is a way to describe deviation from the original pattern in the passive force field.

If the passive force field is so universally available to us in both art and nature we might wonder why we need to work with Bach's flowers at all. But here's the point: the plants he chose are so specific in their representation of emotional states that they are more than just a general placebo. If I take the Bach essence Pine the message is complex and contains many levels of understanding. A textbook says Pine is for guilt and self-blame. But the information in the essence goes more deeply into the question of why and from whence those feelings come. This story of complex emotional entanglement is 'written' in the life history of the pine tree, how it flowers and releases seeds. Study the tree and you will understand the story.[19]

---

19   See *Bach Flower Remedies Form & Function* pages 258-263.

Pine cones releasing the seeds

Having used the word placebo we need to address the subject. It could be that it is all down to the perceived benefit created by the mind. With a placebo it is the message that we are given or which we give ourselves which creates the sense of change and well-being. But the 'placebo effect' so far from discrediting the actions of the Bach flower essences rather proves the point – the power of the passive force field. If the message is 'take this and you will feel better' and it is accepted by me, then it is possible to see how the message of the Rockwater or Impatiens essence may also be accepted by me.

That being the case we might ask: is it really necessary to take essences? And the answer is straightforward. It is a free choice. Bach essences will not enforce change (there is no active chemical ingredient). If you are certain that they will not work then it is very probable that they will not have an effect. When dowsing, if I deny the possibility that it can be real then I will not get a result. You are always in control and can elect to change or not. If you tell yourself that they cannot work – the so-called *nocebo effect* – you are simply closing off the possibilities. Dr Bach even discussed this in the context of the Seven Helpers saying: 'Of course, in all healing there must be a desire in the patient to get well.'[20] It is worth noting, however, that the Bach essences have been found to be effective when used with children and animals and in cases where there is no clear awareness in the subject of the expected beneficial effects. Dr Bach was specific on this point when speaking of Clematis as a treatment for someone unconscious:

> If there is unconsciousness ... Clematis ... [21]
> Ordinary fainting may be of this type and in unconscious cases it is sufficient to moisten the lips with the remedy.[22]

Perhaps it is useful to remember that Dr Bach was a medical doctor and the focus of his life work was to study 'the real cause and cure of disease' – that was the subtitle of his book *Heal Thyself*. But many of us are not directly concerned with disease. Indeed as I mentioned at the beginning it is important, these days, to leave disease and remedies to the doctors. But we can work to understand the direction and meaning of our life and struggle with

20 *Collected Writings of Edward Bach*, FRP, 2007, page 94.

21 Ibid page 62.

22 Ibid page 88.

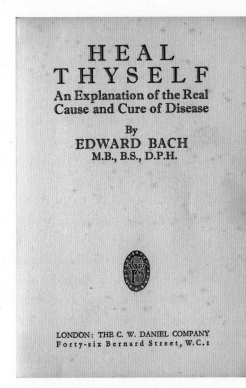

HEAL
THYSELF
An Explanation of the Real
Cause and Cure of Disease

By
EDWARD BACH
M.B., B.S., D.P.H.

LONDON: THE C. W. DANIEL COMPANY
Forty-six Bernard Street, W.C.1

HEAL THYSELF

By
EDWARD BACH, M.B., B.S., D.P.H.

1/6 *net*

An explanation of the real cause
and cure of disease. The author
shows what are the vital principles
which will guide medicine in the
near future, and are indeed guiding
some of the more advanced mem-
bers of the profession to-day. His
book, therefore, comes directly into
the practical politics of medicine.

LONDON
THE C. W. DANIEL COMPANY

internal change. Intervention in that way can help us avoid illness or hasten our recovery. We may come to see what has led us to the place where we are now. That, in turn, may lead to a discovery of who we really are. Perhaps it is a process of equal measure: finding out where we are and discovering who we are.

In Dr Bach's own life it was his cancer in 1917 which triggered a change of perspective. That and the helter-skelter of his personal life. Nora Weeks tells us that he recovered from the surgical operation through determination and commitment to his research work.[23] Perhaps he was lucky. But his desire to understand the real cause and cure of his own disease seems likely to have played a major part. True, he did die 19 years later and today we have no evidence, no statistical analysis or probability otherwise to explain his remission.

We all know that this personal and person-centred experience

23 Weeks, Nora, *Medical Discoveries of Edward Bach*, pages 22-23.

is dismissed as being anecdotal. But the more that I learn about the Bach flowers the more I see individual and personal experience as the key to understanding life. Looking at population statistics or measuring the percentage of people subject to and treated for a particular disease reduces us all to a number. A strong, very strong part of Dr Bach's message was that we must each find our true path in life *as an individual* and thereby take responsibility for what happens to us. But we cannot take responsibility without understanding who and what we are. Working with Dr Bach's ideas and using his flower essences has led me along that path. And I hope and trust that will be a similar journey for you: a journey of self-discovery and self-fulfilment.

So we might return to the question: what is it in the Bach flower essences which helps us to change? Since there is no active chemical ingredient which will work with measurement and analysis it is hard to prove what the vials contain. In an English court of law proof is regarded as 'beyond reasonable doubt'. And in this case it might be argued that after 85 years of practical experience, scientific doubt is itself *unreasonable*. But we must continue with the science of observation. As we better understand how all of us are influenced by information we may make progress in understanding how information may influence our health. The argument here is that flower essences contain information and that information can help us to change. Put simplistically a 'phone call may bring the shock of distressing news, Star of Bethlehem may help us to move back towards balance and peace.

For Bach the context for all his work was his faith in God, a Divine presence in life and what, in a masonic way, he called 'The Name of our Great Master'. We might wonder if that is how he would express matters today. Maybe we have changed the words a little so that 'Divine Providence' is now 'The Gift of Life'; our 'Soul' now our 'Inner Being'. Language adapts and evolves with time. And in part what may have changed is that we see expression of the spiritual world as less localized and more universal: less in the thrones of men, more in the lilies of the field. For Bach the focus of his life work was to bring hope and healing to the sick. In each edition of *The Twelve Healers* he ended with the lines:

> ... the Great Creator of all things, in His Love for us, has placed the herbs in the fields for our healing.[24]

The poet Ezra Pound quotes Richard of Saint Victor:

> *Ubi Amor, ibi Oculus est* – where there is love, there is the eye.

So much of this subject depends upon where we are looking and what we see.

---

24 *Collected Writings of Edward Bach*, FRP, 2007, pages 74, 84, 98.

Bach, Dr Edward, *Collected Writings,* Flower Remedy Programme, second edition 2007.
Ball, Philip, *H2O A Biography of Water,* Weidenfeld & Nicolson, 2009.
Barnard, Julian, *Bach Flower Remedies Form & Function,* Lindisfarne Books, second edition 2004.
— *Bach Flower Remedies the Essence Within,* Winter Press, new edition 2010.
Bartholomew, Alick, *The Story of Water,* Floris Books, 2010.
Blackwood, John, *Geometry in Nature,* Floris Books, 2012.
Blome, Götz, M.D., *Advanced Bach Flower Therapy,* Healing Arts Press, 1999.
Boeser, Knut, *The Elixirs of Nostradamus,* Moyer Bell, 1996.
Briggs, D. & Walters, S. M., *Plant Variation and Evolution,* Cambridge University Press, second edition, 1984.
Buhner, Stephen H., *The Lost Language of Plants,* Chelsea Green Publishing, 2002.
Chamovitz, Daniel, *What a Plant Knows,* Scientific American 2012.
Chaplin, Martin, *Water Structure and Science,* viewable online: http://www1.lsbu.ac.uk/water/memory_of_water.html 2007, 2016. http://www1.lsbu.ac.uk/water/homeopathy.html 2001, 2015.
Coats, Callum, *Living Energies,* Gateway, 2001.
Cortella, Carlo K. & others, *L'Acqua Specchio della Vita,* Editoriale Delfino, 2006.
Critchlow, Keith, *The Hidden Geometry of Flowers,* Floris Books, 2011.
— *Order in Space,* Thames & Hudson, 1969.
Emoto, Masaru, *Messages from Water,* HADO Kyoikusha Co., n.d.
Favareau, David, *Essential Readings of Biosemiotics,* Springer. Viewable online: https://web.natur.cuni.cz/filosof/markos/Publikace/FAVAREAU%20Essential%20Readings%20in%20Biosemiotics.pdf

Gleick, James, *The Information,* Fourth Estate, 2011.

Goldsworthy, Andy, *Rivers & Tides,* DVD, Artificial Eye, Thomas Reidelsheimer 2002.

Graves, Julia *The Language of Plants,* Lindisfarne *Books,* 2012.

Guzmán, Patricio, Director, *The Pearl Button,* (film) 2015.

Jenny, Hans, *Cymatics a Study of Wave Phenomena & Vibration,* Macromedia Publishing, 2001.

King, John, *Reaching for the Sun,* Cambridge University Press, second edition 2011.

Kohn, Eduardo, *How Forests Think,* University of California Press, 2013.

Lilly, Sue, *The Essence Practitioner,* Singing Dragon, 2015.

Lipton, Bruce, *The Biology of Belief,* Elite Books, 2005.

Norland Misha, *Signatures, Miasms, AIDS, Spiritual Aspects of Homoeopathy,* Yondercott Press, 2003.

Perry, Frank, *Himalayan Sound Revelations,* Polair Publishing, 2013.

Pfeiffer, Ehrenfried, *Sensitive Crystallization Processes, a demonstration of the formative forces in the blood,* Anthroposophic Press, 1975.

Steel, Edward, J., *Lamarck's Signatures,* Perseus Books, 1998.

Weeks, Nora, *The Medical Discoveries of Edward Bach Physician,* C. W. Daniel, 1940.

Wilson, Edward O., *Biophilia,* Harvard University Press, 1984.

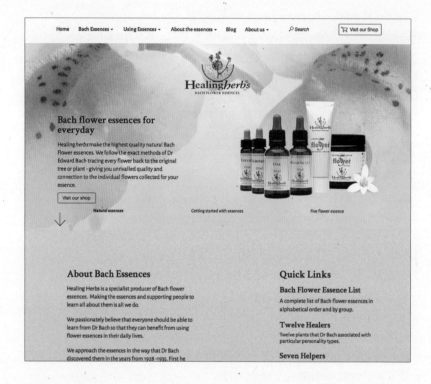

Our website www.healingherbs.co.uk has information about the Bach essences and how to select the most appropriate personal combination. There are also a full set of images of the flowers and audio track recordings by Nickie Murray about the individual remedies.

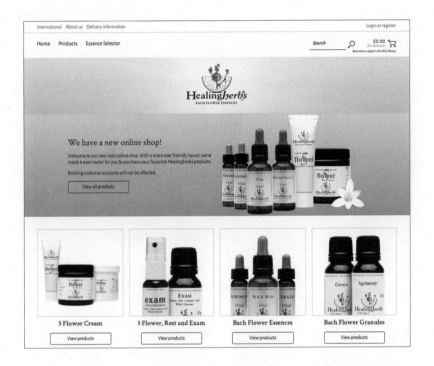

Our new online shop can be viewed at <u>www.healingherbsdirect.</u> <u>co.uk</u> – here you can select from the full range of our products. We usually ship the same day as we receive your order and can send to all countries except USA and Mexico where import restrictions apply.

The Bach Educational Resource is a free to view library of films, audio tracks and books which give background information on the Bach flower essences. Go to www.bacheducationalresource.org and select the language which you wish to work with. You can chose from English, French, German, Italian, Portuguese, Latvian, Spanish, Chinese and Japanese.

Getting to know the Essence

Watch the Impatiens film on the Bach Educational Resource. If anything about the plant catches your attention, make a note of it. As you work through the programme the signature will have more meaning. (GLP_5.18a)
http://bacheducationalresource.org/r/d/18/impatiens

Listen to Nickie Murray talking about this flower and how these types can suffer specifically from mental tension.
http://www.healingherbs.co.uk/essences/essence/impatiens#.VoFr_ChqNmQ

Study the Impatiens Overview to discover what Dr Bach himself wrote about this essence.
http://www.healingherbs.co.uk/essences/essence/impatiens#.VoFr_ChqNmQ

Watch the History of Rescue Remedy on Bach Educational Resource, as Impatiens is in this formula
http://bacheducationalresource.org/r/d/334/the-history-of-the-five-flower-remedy

This new website provides a full guided-learning-programme as an introduction to the Bach flower essences. All the material is free to view and although there is no certificate or qualification you will be led towards a deeper understanding of how the Bach essences work. www.bachflowerlearning.com